Pitman New Era Shorthand Shorthand

Pitman New Era Shorthand

Facility Drills

(Key in Longhand)

Anniversary Edition

Julie Watson

PITMAN PUBLISHING
128 Long Acre, London WC2E 9AN

© Sir Isaac Pitman Limited 1988

British Library Cataloguing in Publication Data
Watson, Julie
  Pitman New Era Shorthand. Facility Drills – Anniversary Edition.
  1. New Era shorthand – Questions & answers
  1. Title
  653′.42

ISBN 0 273 02904 5

Printed and bound by Antony Rowe Ltd,

Contents

Introduction

This *Facility Drills* book should be used in conjunction with the *Pitman New Era Shorthand: Anniversary Edition*.

The objectives are:

1 to reinforce the theory and vocabulary learned in the theory book.
2 to promote speedy and accurate writing of outlines from carefully controlled dictation.
3 to build confidence in writing continuous dictation right from Unit 1, based, as far as possible, on a modern business vocabulary.

The 20 drills are graded to correspond with the 20 units of the *Anniversary Edition*. Except for the very early stages, the format is as follows:

1 Short form and phrase drill followed by continuous practice of those short forms in context.
2 Vocabulary drill followed by continuous practical dictation of that vocabulary in context.

How to use the book

1 Read a line of printed shorthand.
2 Copy this with precision onto the first blank line.
3 Compare your shorthand *critically* with the printed shorthand.
4 Repeat steps 2 and 3 using the remaining blank lines, aiming to improve speed and accuracy with each attempt.

If possible, try to write from the spoken word, since this is your ultimate objective. The *Facility Drills*, used daily, will help you to achieve speed and accuracy in Pitman Shorthand.

Drill 1

Short form, phrase and vocabulary drill

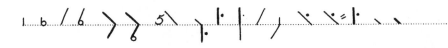

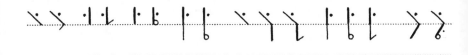

Practical dictation

Simple instructions

1

2

3

Drill 2

Short form, phrase and vocabulary drill

Practical dictation

1 Failure to pay a debt

2 Reluctance to judge a boat show

Drill 3

Short form and phrase drill

Practical dictation

Error in January wage cheque

Vocabulary drill

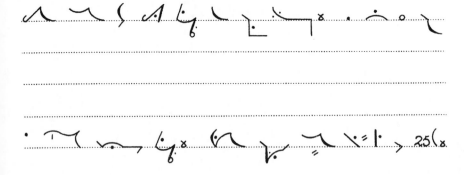

Practical dictation

Changes in the wages department

Drill 3

6

(shorthand symbols)

Drill 4

Short form and phrase drill

(shorthand symbols)

(shorthand symbols)

Practical dictation

Delay in payment of outstanding debt

(shorthand symbols)

Vocabulary drill

Practical dictation

Instructions for purchase of language tapes

Organising an office lunch

Drill 5

Short form and phrase drill

Practical dictation

Fund raising for a local gala

Vocabulary drill

[shorthand outlines]

Practical dictation _____

Query about a bill

[shorthand outlines]

Selecting a suitable software package

Drill 6

Short form and phrase drill

Practical dictation

Diversification into new product areas

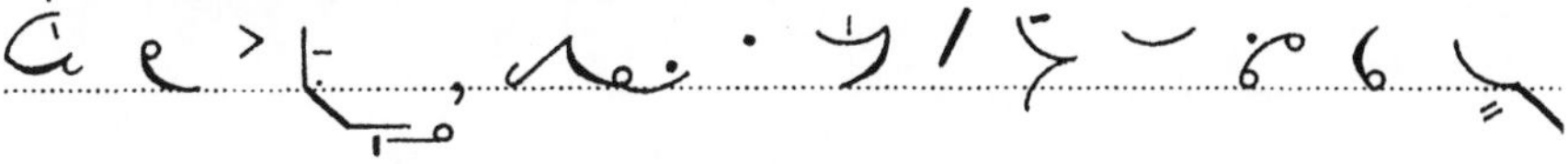

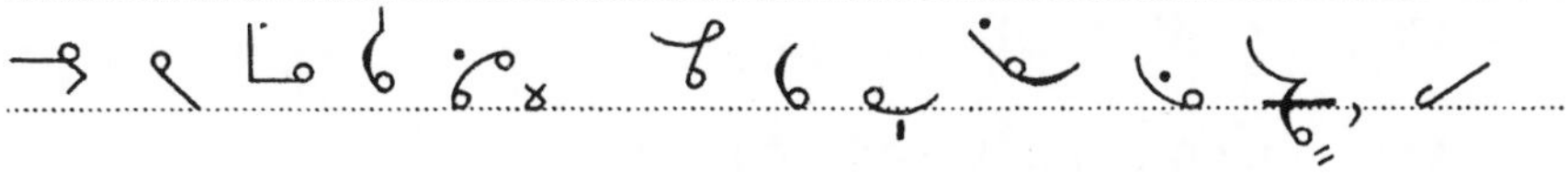

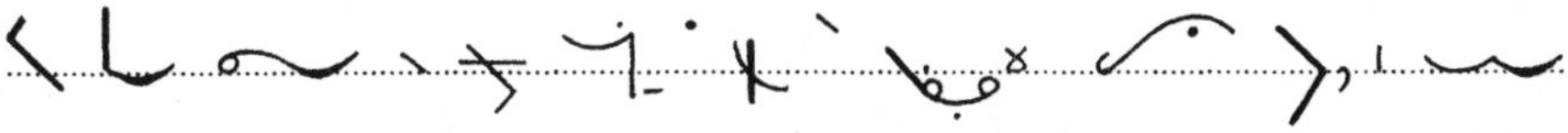

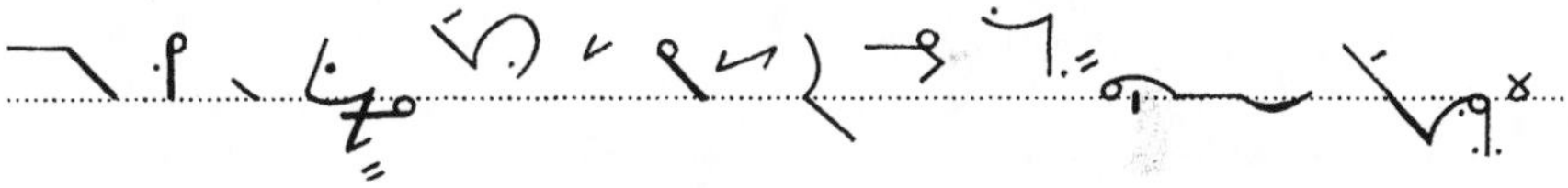

Vocabulary drill

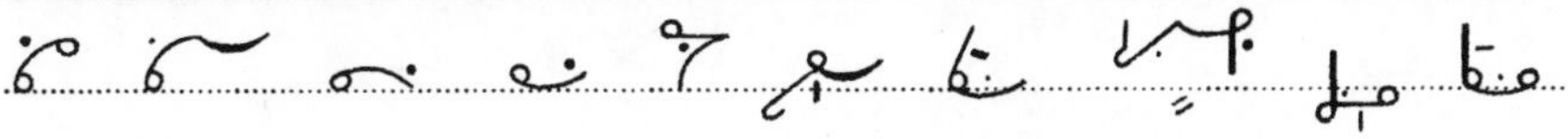

(shorthand outline)

Practical dictation

New techniques to increase sales

(shorthand outlines)

Drill 7

Short form and phrase drill

[Shorthand outlines]

Practical dictation

A bank loan to fund a new business deal

[Shorthand outlines]

Vocabulary drill

Practical dictation

Review of safety regulations at a factory

Drill 8

Short form and phrase drill

Practical dictation

Memorandum regarding change in sales policy

Practical dictation _____

New techniques to increase sales

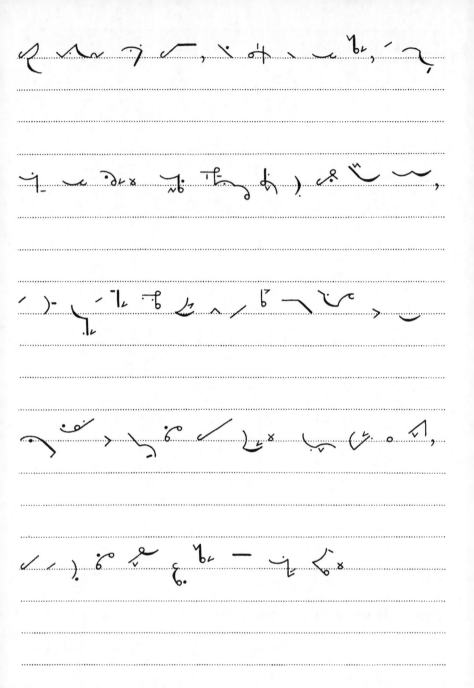

Drill 9

Short form and phrase drill

Practical dictation _____

Failure by manufacturer to deliver goods on time

Vocabulary drill

Practical dictation

Extract from holiday brochure

Drill 10

Short form and phrase drill

(shorthand outlines)

Practical dictation

Farewell party for Sales Manager

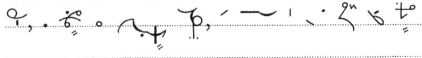

Vocabulary drill

Practical dictation

Purchase of a new computer

Drill 11

Practical dictation

Checking qualifications for a secretarial appointment

Vocabulary drill

25) [shorthand symbols]

Practical dictation _____

Recruitment of new Marketing Manager

[shorthand symbols]

[shorthand symbols]

[shorthand symbols]

35 [shorthand symbols]

Drill 12

Short form and phrase drill

Practical dictation

Extract from a Chairman's address

Vocabulary drill—1

(shorthand outlines)

Practical dictation

Oversight in payment of account

(shorthand outlines)

1,730 23

Vocabulary drill—2

Practical dictation

Comments on strike negotiations

Short form and phrase drill

Practical dictation

Comparison of regional sales

Vocabulary drill—1

(shorthand outlines)

Practical dictation

Letter regarding new current account facility

(shorthand outlines)

Vocabulary drill—2

Practical dictation

Comments regarding potential take-over bid

Drill 14

Short form and phrase drill

(shorthand outlines)

Practical dictation

Letter requesting computer training

(shorthand outlines)

Vocabulary drill

[Shorthand outlines]

Practical dictation

Letter regarding insurance cover for lost jewellery

[Shorthand outlines]

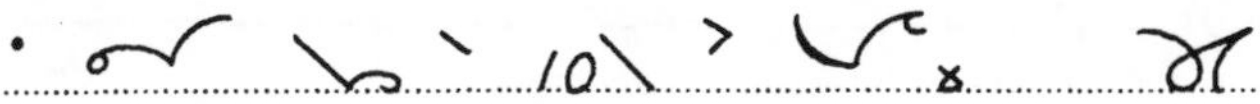

Drill 15

Short form and phrase drill

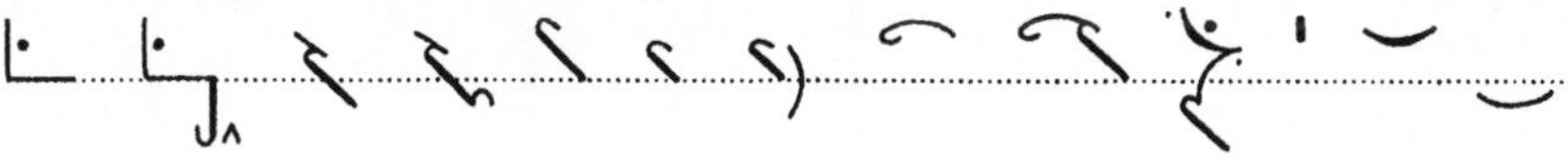

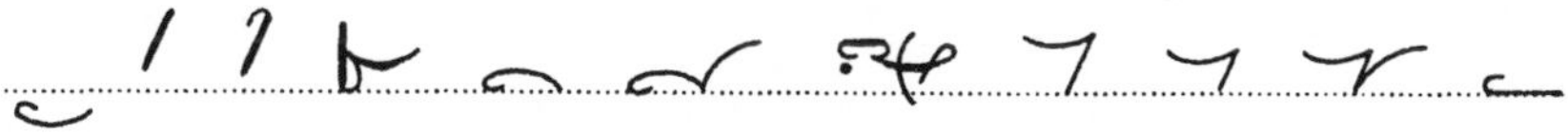

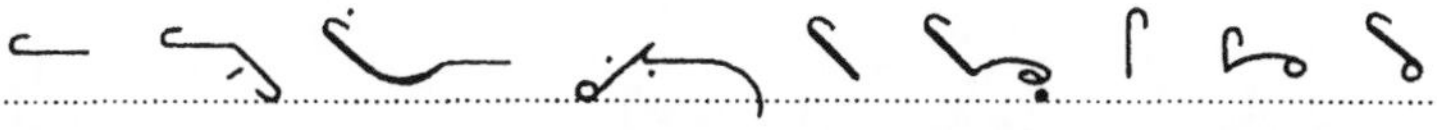

Practical dictation

Circular letter advising of a new building society account

(shorthand outlines)

Practical dictation _____

Letter regarding car fleet replacement

Practical dictation _____

Memorandum giving instructions to renovate reception area

Drill 16

Short form and phrase drill

Practical dictation

Competition between banks and building societies

Vocabulary drill—1

Practical dictation ⎯⎯⎯⎯⎯⎯⎯⎯

Letter regarding new techniques for staff briefing

Vocabulary drill—2

Practical dictation

Letter regarding a faulty cordless telephone

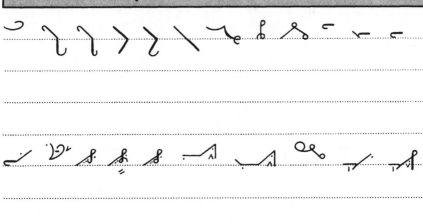

Drill 17

Short form and phrase drill

Practical dictation

Residents' pressure group to preserve countryside

Practical dictation

Application for post of Fashion Editor

Drill 18

Short form and phrase drill

(shorthand outlines)

Practical dictation

Letter of apology for failure to deliver goods

(shorthand outlines)

Practical dictation _____

Memorandum issuing threat of dismissal

Drill 19

Short form and phrase drill

(shorthand outlines)

Practical dictation

Letter giving customer details of special offer

(shorthand outlines)

Practical dictation

Instructions regarding stationery requisition

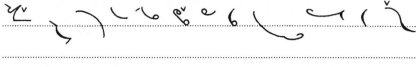

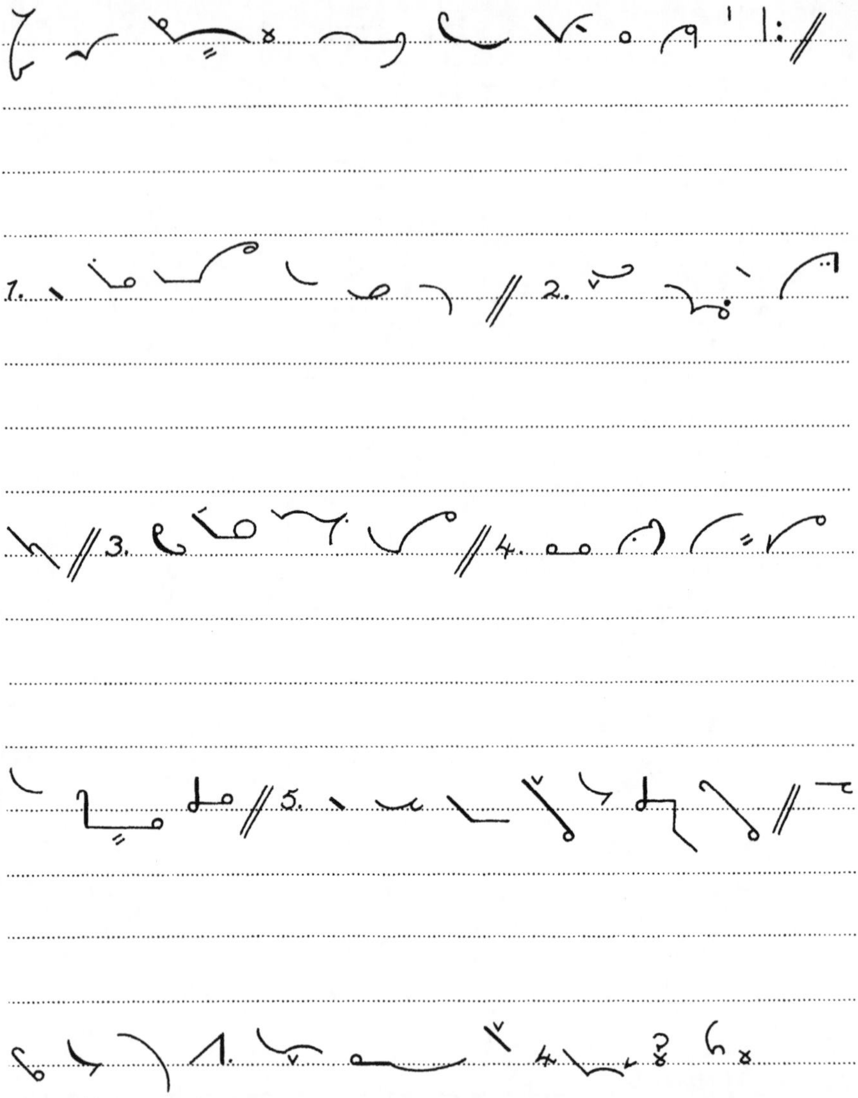

Drill 20

Practical dictation

Commercial television advertising

Vocabulary drill—1

Practical dictation

Feasibility study on central computer unit

Vocabulary drill—2

Practical dictation

Bank's letter confirming customer's credit requirements

(shorthand outlines)

Key

Drill 1

Short form, phrase and vocabulary drill

be, be the, do, do the, which, which the, to, to the, to, to do the, is, is the, is, is to, it, it is, it, is it, who, who is, but, but is, which, which is, object, objects, 5 per cent today, day, debt, which, but which, pay, pay-day, to, two, pay, pay the, aid, aid the, day, days, date, dates, pay, paid, paid the, date, dates, date the, page, pages, page the, tape, tapes, tape the.

Practical dictation _____

Simple instructions

1   Date the page. But which page? Date page 2. Do / it today! *(12 words)*
2   Today is pay-day. The debt is to be paid. / Pay 40 per cent today. *(15 words)*
3   Do the pages today. The object is to tape the / pages, but who is to be paid to do it?
    (20 words)

Drill 2

they, they think, they have, them, them the, shall, shall the, shall be, shall be the, usually, February, was, owes, us, say, say the, fed, fetch, fetch the, be, both, is, 30th, debt, debts, Dutch.

Practical dictation

1 Failure to pay a debt
Who owes us the debts? Say they have to the / 30th to pay both the debts. They have paid us / 10 per cent but 90 per cent is owed to / us. They have both objected, but it is up to / us to say the debts shall be paid. *(48 words)*

2 Reluctance to judge a boat show
It was up to them to judge the usual February / Boat Show but they both objected. They usually do it, / but they say they think it is up to the / Dutch to do it. *(34 words)*

Drill 3

Short form and phrase drill

we, wage, wages department, we think, we have, we do, we shall, we never, we informed the, November, they, they will, who will, it will, which will, they will be, it will be, which will be, who will be the, it will be the, which will have the, to, to give, to give the, given the, to come, thing, to, to do, to do the, is, is to, is the, two cheques, January, November, Dale Company Limited.

Practical dictation

Error in January wage cheque
His January wage cheque was too low. The wages department / was never informed. They will have to give him two / cheques come February pay-day to make it up. We / informed the wages department today. They say it is an / unusual thing to do, but they will do it. *(49 words)*

Vocabulary drill

no, inform, cheque, cheques, two cheques, to, to aim, to make, to take, take the, effect, effects, month, memo, name, to delay, to delay the, be, below, too low.

Practical dictation _____

Changes in the wages department
We have informed them the wage changes have to take / effect. The aim is to have a month to make / the changes. They will have to delay the November pay- / day to the 25th. Take the memo to the / wages department. They will name the day to give the / departments the changes. *(53 words)*

Drill 4

Short form and phrase drill

we think, they think, they do, they do the, we have, we shall have, give, give the, for, for them, on, on the, but, but the, with, with the, large, all, all the, also, who, owing (language), languages, had, a (an), and, and the, as, as the.

Practical dictation _____

Delay in payment of outstanding debt
We have informed them of the debt owing to us / but they have objected to the January pay date. They / had the thing on the 5th November. We usually give / them a month to pay — and we also give them / 10 per cent off for cash. They have had long / enough to pay all of the debt. *(57 words)*

Vocabulary drill

for, follow, follow the, among, among the, at, at the, to, to take, to take away, path, package, packages, back, bank, large, job, jobs, shop, shops, ask, long, lunch.

Practical dictation _____

Instructions for purchase of language tapes
The tapes may be bought at the shop up at / the top of the path. The shop has language tapes / among the tapes on show. Ask the shop for the / language tape packages. The backs of the packages also give / facts on jobs with languages. *(45 words)*

Organising an office lunch
They say it will be a long talk which is / to be given at the bank, so we shall have / to follow it with lunch. Ask them to get the / lunch for us. The bank is to give us a / cheque to pay for it, as the talk is given / at the bank. *(53 words)*

Drill 5

Short form and phrase drill

difference, wish, wish the, put, put the, to be, to be the, on, on the, can, can the, go, ought, who, and, in the, any, anything, nothing, had, do, different, we shall, we wish, put, be, to be, owe, owing, thing, young, have, have the, to have the, on which, on which the, we have no, to give, village bank, of cash, to get, they, they have no, different policy, to give the party, which the bank.

Practical dictation
Fund raising for a local gala

We shall have to put on a gala with a / difference for the young in the autumn. We ought to / have a theme we can follow for the party. As / usual we have nothing in the bank to pay for / it, so we shall have to ask the village bank / to give us the money to get the thing moving. / They have never objected to us asking for anything if / we make it a policy to keep them informed. *(79 words)*

Vocabulary drill

to be, bill, bit, booking, meal, deal, team, nobody, look, into, feed the, ease, each, date, data, data bank, mail, mailing.

Practical dictation
Query about a bill

They have objected to the bill which they had to / pay for the meal. They say it was too large, / but nobody objected on the day they paid. We ought / to make a check on the food they had. We / took many parties on the 5th, which was the date / they came, but if we wish them to keep the / booking for 10th January, we shall have to look into / the bill. *(72 words)*

Selecting a suitable software package

We think we ought to look into ways of having / the detail of the company's mailing put in an up- / to-date data bank. We ought to get a package / into which we may feed the detail of the monthly / wages. It ought also to do the mailing with ease, / and to give us a copy of all the data / each month. We wish to have a package which is / also easy to load. *(74 words)*

Drill 6

Short form and phrase drill

as, as the, several, because, because of the, on those, on this, thus, much, as much as, as much as possible, in as much as, so much, which, which seems, for sale, this will, different, subject, special, speaks, with us, something, especially.

Practical dictation _____

Diversification into new product areas

Along with several of the tobacco companies, we have seen / an unusually large fall in sales this February because of / the special tax on those sales. In as much as / this is no passing phase for this Government, we ought / to be doing something to put the company into a / different form of business. We may object, but nothing can / be said to change the Government's policy on the subject, / especially because of the anti-smoking publicity. *(77 words)*

Practical dictation _____

New techniques to increase sales

The sales techniques which the sales team is using this / month seem to be succeeding in selling dozens of office / desks to the big companies in the city. The saving / of 15 per cent for each desk bought on the / same day is the chosen sales pitch which seems to / be making the difference. The boss is asking for a / full scale attack on the small business scene, using the / same techniques. On Wednesday we shall be discussing the form / it will take. *(83 words)*

Drill 7

Practical dictation _____

A bank loan to fund a new business deal

As far as we can see, the guarantee requirements which / the bank is asking for seem to be satisfactory and / we can make arrangements for the money to go to / the dealers in the form of a cheque. It is / our policy never to go into the red at the / bank, but this deal is something which we should take / up. Your business ability is a bonus to this Company, / and we wish to say thanks for the hours put / in on this business deal. *(85 words)* safety, office, officer, service, door, fact, factory, narrow, rules, remedy, alarm, error, rung, four, fourth, 4th, injuries, rush, memo, memory, fear, ensure, thorough, thorough policy.

Practical dictation

Review of safety regulations at a factory
The safety officer had said the service door at the / rear of the factory was too narrow and below the / requirements set in the Government rules. A remedy for this / ought to be put into effect as early as possible. / On Saturday the 4th, the alarm was rung in error, / but the rush to the service door to escape caused / several injuries. We should ensure thorough policy changes at the / company because of the memory of this fear and panic. *(80 words)*

Drill 8

Short form and phrase drill

beyond, beyond my, beyond me, I, I came, I will, I am, I may, why, do, do you, what, what you, when, when you, are, are you, with, with you, can, can you, give, give you, 50 per cent per annum, to, to speak, to you, to get, how, me, him, some, some attention, now, now charge.

Practical dictation

Memorandum regarding change in sales policy
It is beyond my ability to make sales rise by / 50 per cent per annum. Earlier this year, when I / came to speak to you of my idea for a / new sales policy, it was satisfactory at the time. Why / do you now ask me for something different? How do / you think I can do what you ask with so / few facilities to get things moving? We shall have to / do as much as possible with what we have got / now, and you will have to put any ideas for / big policy changes on ice! *(95 words)*

Vocabulary drill

for, for my, right, rise, rising, desire, toy, toys, toy business, buy, buying, now, nowadays, to review, to review the, new, news, value, idea, ideas, area, areas, video, audio, see, seeing, real, really, survive, to survive, theory.

Practical dictation _____

New techniques to increase sales
If we are really going to survive in the toy / business in years to come, it is obvious we shall / have to review the image we give, pay some attention / to new ideas, and move into new areas. Nowadays customers / desire easy ways of buying anything, and so video and / audio cassettes showing how our toys can be of value / to the young may be the answer to the poor / sales we are seeing. If my theory is right, we / should see sales rising when these ideas go into the / shops. *(91 words)*

Drill 9

Short form and phrase drill

was, whose, for, for us, for the society, for whom, I hope, and I hope, I hope you will be, we hope, we hope you are, he will, would, would you, manufacture (manufactured), manufacturer, if, if he, if he would, this, this time, give, gives, gives the, too, too much, of, of having, should, should be, we shall be, they will have, pick up.

Practical dictation _____

Failure by manufacturer to deliver goods on time
The items for the society should be here for us / to pick up tomorrow, and I hope this time they / will be ready! Would you give the manufacturer a ring / and inform him we shall be at the factory at / two? I hope you will be firm with him if / he gives the usual excuse of having too much to / do at this time of year. If he speaks of / a delay, cancel the whole deal. *(76 words)*

Vocabulary drill

high, highly, hotels, history, handy, hustle, ahead, holiday, visitors, health, hall, whom, neighbourhood, capacity.

Practical dictation _____

Extract from holiday brochure
In high season the hotels in the neighbourhood are full / to capacity with holiday visitors who wish to take in / the history of the area. Besides this, the health farm / at the Hall is highly popular, especially with those in / the city, for whom it is a handy refuge for / relaxing out of the hustle of city life. We hope / you will go ahead and book your holiday; we can / assure you of a happy time here! *(77 words)*

Drill 10

Short form and phrase drill

all, though, although, always, also, most, almost, influence, influenced, large, largest, my, myself, him, himself, as fast as, it, itself, them, themselves, our market, ourselves, as is, as we know, as we know the, as we are, as we are sorry, as we think, this is, in this city, as soon as, as soon as possible, as well as, first.

Practical dictation

Farewell party for Sales Manager

As we know, the Sales Manager is leaving the Department / in this city, and going on to a higher post / at the Company's Head Office. I think it would be / nice if, as his sales staff, we put on a / special leaving party for him ourselves, as we are sorry / to see him go. I will get the food, although / I hope you will all give as much as you / can for this, as well as for a cheque which / I hope to give him at the party. Next Wednesday, / the first, would seem to be the best date for / this party. What do you think? *(106 words)*

Vocabulary drill

we must, fast, faster, store, storage, devise, devised, list, test, tests, use, used, assess, access, text, suggest, I suggest, basis, analyst, research.

Practical dictation

Purchase of a new computer

We must buy something different which can access data faster / and with a storage capacity which can cope with the / volume of text which we now have. Our analyst has / devised a list of tests which can be used to / assess what is on this market, although cost obviously must / form the basis of our choice. I suggest you research / the subject as soon as possible as we wish to / get moving on this. *(74 words)*

Drill 11

Short form and phrase drill

as soon as, as we have, word, words, let us have, to let us have the, to let you have the, I would, I would like you, this would, it would be, at the same time, for some time, carried out, if it is, if it is possible, it is not possible, sent, be sent, quite, under, could, could you, could be, that, without, without this, immediate, immediately, certificates, national policy, such enquiries.

Practical dictation _____

Checking qualifications for a secretarial appointment

As soon as you have your certificates for one hundred / and twenty *stroke* fifty words a minute, let us have / sight of them and they will be sent back to / you immediately. You can quite see that it is not / possible to let you have the post without this check / being carried out, as we have to be certain that / you could do the job. At the same time, I / would not like you to think that I doubt your / word, but it is the policy of the company that / such enquiries are made.   *(94 words)*

Practical dictation _____

Recruitment of new Marketing Manager

The Marketing Manager has handed in his notice this morning / so we must give immediate attention to the search for / a likely candidate. Type out a detailed sheet indicating exactly / what we would like the successful candidate to have. He / *stroke* she should be smart, highly educated, be about thirty- / five years old, and with recent, first-hand expertise in / the field. The post gives all the usual Company benefits. / All details must be received by the 25th of / this month. *(82 words)*

Drill 12

Practical dictation _____

Extract from a Chairman's address

I would like to say a few words to members / on the Company Report which you have before you. You / will remember that last year I was most surprised to / have to remark on the decreasing sales. However, this year / it gives me very much pleasure to report an increase / in sales of 25 per cent, which is principally / due to the very large efforts of the marketing team / in our overseas markets. I will give you a very / short description of policy so far, before passing you over / to the Marketing Manager. *(94 words)*

I, I regret, I trust, accord (according), according to the, records, over, overlooked, effort, normal, normal policy, credit, afraid, agree, measures, according, accordingly, debt, debtors, more, no more, granted, it would appear, April.

Practical dictation _____

Oversight in payment of account
Dear Sir, I regret to inform you that according to / our records it would appear that you have overlooked our / invoice number 1730 dated 23 April. / I trust you will make every effort to pay this / sum since it is not the normal policy of the / company to give credit. I am afraid that unless you / agree to pay the debt by the 24th of / this month, I shall have to take measures accordingly and / to put you on our debtors' list. In that case, / no more goods could ever be sent to you. Yours / faithfully *(101 words)*

Vocabulary drill — 2

managers, at, liberty, at liberty, so far, so far as, according to, according to the, brake, strike, striking, engineers, industry, it seems, it seems the, there, offer, if it is possible, if it is not possible, and if it is not possible, agree, to agree, with, withdraw, progress, to solve, to solve the, labour, dispute, press.

Practical dictation _____

Comments on strike negotiations
The managers are not at liberty to speak on the / talks so far but, according to the press, this is / 'make or break' time for the striking engineers in the / industry. It seems the managers have made their last offer / and if it is not possible for the engineers to / agree to this, they will withdraw from the talks and / no more progress can be made to solve the labour / dispute. *(71 words)*

Drill 13

Short form and phrase drill

it would appear, it appears, I think, I think it is, because, because of the, I can, I can assure you, carried, carried on, carried out, going, going on, what, what is, in all parts, of the country, within, within the, northern, southern, lower, lower than, opinion, in my opinion, their (there), their own, they are, different, have, have been.

Practical dictation

Comparison of regional sales

It would appear that the Sales Manager in the northern / region is generally surprised at what is going on in / different parts of the country, especially within the southern area. / His sales tend to be lower than they are in / the south. In my opinion, I think it is because / of the limited amount of Head Office influence to which / they are subjected. Things have been allowed to get out / of hand. However, I can assure you that from now / on things are to be carried out in a very / different manner. *(92 words)*

Vocabulary drill — 1

Mr, Mrs, draw, drawn, is, is known, arrange, arranging, overdraw, overdrawn, open, down, earn, earning, earnings, return the form, dependent, current, account, this account, your account, joint, amount, amounts, demand, demands, event, urgent, to extend, determine, determined, facilities, expenditure.

Practical dictation

Letter regarding new current account facility

Dear Mr and Mrs Brown, Your attention is drawn to / our new current account facility which is being organised to / cut down the time taken to arrange facilities to overdraw / an account in the event of urgent expenditure. This facility / is known as being 'in the pink'. If you open / this account, it means that you can be overdrawn up / to an amount which is previously determined and, of course, / dependent on your joint earnings. If you wish to extend / this facility to your account, just fill in and return / the form below. Yours sincerely *(95 words)*

Vocabulary drill — 2

I have, I have been, you will, you will not, you will not be, I am not, I do not, I did not, that he is, that he is not, it would be, it would not be, what has been, Tuesday, Tuesday next, opinion, in my opinion, in our opinion, in his opinion, chair, chaired, chairman, our, our own, happen, their own, to learn, keen, abandon, better than, habit, stand, surprise, surprised, good policy, in this view.

Practical dictation

Comments regarding potential take-over bid

I have been talking to the Chairman about the take-over / to be discussed by the Board on Tuesday next. You / will not be surprised to learn that he is not / keen that this should happen now. In his opinion, results / have been better than last year and it would not / be good policy to abandon what has been fought for / now the outlook is better than before. I am not / happy to see us do so either, and I do / not think we shall be on our own in this / view. How do you stand on this? *(97 words)*

Drill 14

Short form and phrase drill

on Wednesday, on Wednesday next, I am, I am not, I do, I do not, I expect, I would, I hope, I practise, together with, of their, there will be, at the same time, at the time, altogether, this would be, they use, university, familiar, system, someone, hardware, software, while, worth while, work.

Practical dictation _____

Letter requesting computer training

Dear Sir, I start work at the university on Wednesday / next but I am not altogether familiar with the software / they use. I expect I will have to practise for / a short while to get familiar with the system and / the hardware. At the same time, however, I hope there / will be someone there who can give me the benefit / of their expertise together with their opinion of the system / and how it works. I think that practice on this / would be worth while before I start work and I / would find it most useful. Yours faithfully *(97 words)*

Vocabulary drill

white, anywhere, elsewhere, whilst, we are, aware, you were, worry, worth, world, warranties, worn, subsequent, goodwill, willing, insurance policy, from the beginning.

Practical dictation _____

Letter regarding insurance cover for lost jewellery

Dear Miss White, Whilst we are obviously aware of your / loss and the subsequent worry which it has caused, your / insurance policy in no way covers jewellery of such worth / worn anywhere in this country or elsewhere in the world / without special warranties being agreed with the insurance company. You / were aware of this from the beginning. However, as a / gesture of goodwill the company is willing to make a / small payment of 10 per cent of the value. Yours / sincerely *(81 words)*

Drill 15

Short form and phrase drill

take, take down, I believe, I believe you, able, able to (build/building), building society, more (remark/remarked), remarkable, available, owe, owing, own, owner, large, largely, distinguish (distinguished), Mr (mere), merely, granting us the authority, in which, in which it, in which it will, equal (equally), call, call upon, blank, circular, by all, by all means, at all, at all times, balance.

Practical dictation

Circular letter advising of a new building society account

Subject: New building society account. Dear 'blank', I wish to / draw your attention to our remarkable new account which is / available to both home and non-home owners. It acts / largely like a current account but the difference is easily / distinguished because each month you will see your balance grow / by merely granting us the authority to put 10 per / cent of your net earnings into a different account in / which it will accrue a return equal to the usual / building society rates. By all means give us a call / to discuss this — we are available at all times. Yours / sincerely *(101 words)*

Vocabulary drill — 1

fleet, replacement, and I, believe you, possible, possibly, suitable, black, blue, cloth, plus, glass, models, tinted, deliver (delivery), take, take place, place, supply, supply the, please, enclose, enclosing, interior, extras, windows, of, of price, short, shortly.

Practical dictation

Letter regarding car fleet replacement

Dear Sir, Our car fleet is due for replacement and / I believe you have a new range of models which / might possibly be suitable for our needs. The whole fleet / must be in blue and black, with a blue cloth / interior, plus all the usual extras. Three cars should be / the luxury models with tinted windows. Delivery must take place / within the next two months. If you can supply the / cars, please write to me enclosing details of price, and / I will be in touch shortly. Yours faithfully *(88 words)*

Vocabulary drill—2

call, call upon the, at all, at all times, by all means, entitle, entitled, total, plan, reasonable, delicate, delicately, reflect, basically, practical, I want, flowers, approval, plants, prints, client, clients, artificial, essential, display, budget, designer, disgrace, prepare, permit, décor, visual, walls.

Practical dictation

Memorandum giving instructions to renovate reception area

Memo to the Office Manager, entitled: 'Client waiting area — a / total disgrace'. Would you prepare a décor plan for my / approval. Basically, I want to see practical ideas within reasonable / expenditure limits which will reflect our new visual image to / clients. A display of artificial plants and flowers is essential. / Possibly the walls should be delicately painted, with prints on / them. By all means call upon the services of an / interior designer if the budget will permit this. *(78 words)*

Drill 16

Short form and phrase drill

able to (build/building), to build, building society, mortgage, mortgage business, within the, our, our own, our own policy, in our, can, cannot, we cannot, danger, danger of, difficult, difficulty, advantage, never, nevertheless, large, larger, largely, tried, they have tried, what is, going on, financial (financially), neglect (neglected), capitalise, distinguish (distinguished).

Practical dictation

Competition between banks and building societies

Our building society is not in danger of being in / financial difficulty, but nevertheless we should pay attention to what / is going on within the banks. We have seen a / 10 per cent drop in mortgage business over the last / six months and this must be due largely to the / influence of the banks and their recent marketing policy, in / which they have tried to attract new mortgage business. We / cannot neglect our own policy or we shall see the / society's advantage lost. We should capitalise on our distinguished record / and the high opinion that people have of our practice / within the mortgage world. However, at the same time we / must keep an eye on the need to build up / some of the more usual bank services so as to / regain lost business. *(133 words)*

Vocabulary drill — 1

I approve, brief, to brief the, briefing, definite, definitely, provide, photograph, photographs, graphic, effective, informative, observe, active, actively, paragraph, drift, drifts, on Monday afternoon, representative, representatives, rate of, part of, part of the, intend, displays, flip, charts, programme, technical, jargon.

Practical dictation

Letter regarding new techniques for staff briefing

Dear David, I approve of the visual way in which / you intend to brief the new sales representatives on Monday / afternoon. The photographs and graphic displays on the flip charts / will provide an effective and informative briefing medium. I think / we will observe a better rate of recall when it / comes to the part of the programme where they are / actively involved. Paragraph upon paragraph of technical jargon is difficult / to remember and the mind drifts away. Your idea is / definitely better. Well done! Yours sincerely *(86 words)*

Vocabulary drill — 2

I refer, yesterday afternoon, telephone, telephone call, number of, out of, range of, proving, respect (respected), respectful (respectfully), receptive, above, alternative, pamphlet, cord, cordless, fault, faulty, situate, situated, aerial, remedies, free, signals.

Practical dictation

Letter regarding a faulty cordless telephone

Dear Madam, I refer to the message left on our/telephone answering machine yesterday afternoon. I respectfully ask you to/look at paragraph number 6 in the pamphlet supplied with/your cordless telephone. In brief, this gives a number of/reasons why your telephone may be proving faulty. Perhaps you/are either moving out of range of the base unit/when making your telephone calls or your aerial is not/situated high enough above the base unit, thus making it/less receptive to the radio signals. However, if these remedies/fail to be effective, I will arrange to send you/an alternative telephone free of charge. Yours faithfully *(108 words)*

Drill 17

Short form and phrase drill

information, production, productive, object (objected), objection, public (publish/published), investigation, satisfaction, responsible (responsibility), guard, to guard, great, greater, association, resident, Residents' Association, residents, carry out, to carry out, as soon as possible, country, countryside, national press, at the beginning, for the Government, behalf, of their, to raise.

Practical dictation

Residents' pressure group to preserve countryside

Upon appearance of the information in the national press, the/Residents' Association saw it as their responsibility to raise a/public objection to try to guard their local countryside. At/the beginning, their objections were not very productive, for the/Government could see no need to carry out an investigation./However, more pressure from the Association led to greater satisfaction/and the decision was taken to carry out an investigation/as soon as possible on behalf of the residents. *(79 words)*

Vocabulary drill

fashion, motion, information, relation, examinations, extension, profession, professional, addition, additional, application, application form, education, occupation, occupational, discussion, vacation, selection, attention, I draw your attention, objection, organisation, position, appreciate, week, week beginning.

Practical dictation

Application for post of Fashion Editor

Dear Sirs, Please find enclosed my application form for the/position of Fashion Editor within your organisation. I draw your/attention to my curriculum vitae which gives additional information in/relation to my education, professional examinations, and recent occupational experience / within the profession. I would appreciate having a discussion with / you before the selection procedure is put in motion and, / if you have no objection, I am available on extension / 61. However, I am on vacation for one week / beginning 2nd August. Yours faithfully *(85 words)*

Drill 18

Short form and phrase drill

I refer, I can, I can only, I take, I take this, I can assure you, I apologise, to tell you, to meet the, to meet the requirements, systems, Systems plc, Hi-tech Business, your corporation, past few years, next few days, as quickly as possible, will be sent, request, requested, particular, opportunity, experience, experienced.

Practical dictation

Letter of apology for failure to deliver goods
Dear Sir, I refer to your telex which requested delivery / of one monitor as well as two keyboards and your / subsequent enquiry about this. Indeed, over the past few years / Hi-tech Business Systems plc has done much business / with your corporation and I can only apologise for the / delay. May I take this particular opportunity to tell you / that we intend to take steps to improve the delivery / service so that we are able to meet the requirements / of our customers as quickly as possible. I can assure / you that your goods will be sent as soon as / they are available; certainly within the next few days. I / apologise once again for the delays you have experienced. Yours / faithfully *(121 words)*

Vocabulary drill

poor, poorer, first, firstly, second, secondly, third, thirdly, care, cared, careless, imperative, it is imperative, prompt, inadequate, inadequacy, quantity, quality, past few months, next few months, no less than, there must be, mistakes, last time, dismissal, warn, warnings.

Practical dictation

Memorandum issuing threat of dismissal
Over the past few months you have received warnings no / less than twice from me and still your work gets / poorer and poorer. Over the next few months there must / be some improvement! Your work is unsatisfactory on three counts: / firstly, the quantity of items you produce is low; secondly, / the quality is poor; and, thirdly, you make too many / careless mistakes. It is imperative that you take prompt action / this time to improve your work, as this is the / last time you will have the opportunity to do so. / If you do not, these inadequacies will result in your / dismissal. *(101 words)*

Drill 19

Short form and phrase drill

in, in which you, knowledge, knowledge of, acknowledge, wonderful (wonderfully), writer (rather), rather than, interest, other, many other, no other, in our, in order to, in order that, later, no later than, not later than, I think, I think there is, for your letter, some, some other, as much, disappointed, December.

Practical dictation

Letter giving customer details of special offer

Dear Madam, Thank you for your letter dated 10 December / in which you express interest in our wonderful typewriter offer. / This month we have some other unusual bargain offers, as / you will see from the pictures in our enclosed brochure. / Although there are many other typewriters on the market, I / think there is no other which offers as much value / for money as this. Rather than be disappointed, place your / order with us no later than 17 December. Use our / special postal service in order that you can be secure / in the knowledge that one has been reserved for you. / Thank you for your interest. Yours faithfully *(107 words)*

Vocabulary drill

afternoon, every, everything, order, in order to, in order that, hold, holder, fold, folder, calendars, later, not later than, leather, signature, directors, bind, binder, binders, print, printers, September, dozen, I would like, middle, letterhead, letter-headed.

Practical dictation

Instructions regarding stationery requisition

I would like to have the order for office supplies / sent this afternoon in order that they arrive not later / than the middle of September. Make sure everything below is / listed on it:

1 Two packets of calendars for next / year.
2 Nine reams of letterheaded paper.
3 Seven boxes / of manilla folders.
4 Six leather letter-holders for Directors' / desks.
5 Two new book binders for the desk-top / printers.

Can you please have the order ready for my / signature by 4 pm? Thank you. *(87 words)*

Drill 20

individual, prospects, advertisement (advertise, advertised), advertisements, advertising, commercial, regular, be, come, become, becoming, in, income, well, come, welcome, welcoming, inconvenience (inconvenient, inconveniently), $18\frac{3}{4}\%$, $19\frac{1}{4}\%$, magnitude, circumstance, circumstances, in the circumstances, instruct, instructive, instruction, practice, probable (probably/probability), governed (govern), government, this Government.

Practical dictation

Commercial television advertising
In the beginning, individual Board members did not like the / prospect of advertising on commercial TV because they did / not wish to become committed to such high expenditure on / a regular basis. However, their opinions had been altered by / the sales increases for June of $18\frac{3}{4}$ / per cent and July of $19\frac{1}{4}$ per / cent, which were of sufficient magnitude to convince them of / the value of advertising. In the circumstances, they issued the / instruction that the practice should continue since the increase was / in all probability due to the impact of the advertisements. *(100 words)*

instruct, instructed, possible, possibility, desirability, feasibility, meeting, meetings, transferring, hearing, departmental, psychological, majority, majority of, computer, computers, communications, improve communications, connection, considerable, contest, will contest, confident, I am confident, contained, self-contained, commence, in order to commence, achievement, forward, hardship.

Practical dictation

Feasibility study on central computer unit
We have been instructed to carry out a feasibility study / into the possibility, or indeed desirability, of transferring our departmental / computer operations to one self-contained computer unit. This is / to be done in order to rationalise accommodation and improve / communications within the company. Although it is a mission of / considerable magnitude which I feel the majority of staff will / contest for psychological reasons, I am confident it will be / effected. Its achievement should be fairly easy, without too much / inconvenience or hardship during the changeover. Can you attend a / meeting on Wednesday afternoon of this week in order to / commence discussions? I look forward to hearing from you in / this connection. *(112 words)*

£5, £2000, £5000, rate of, rate of interest, constitutes, 19.7%, 18½%, 18½% per annum, 1½%, quarter, half.

Practical dictation

Bank's letter confirming customer's credit requirements

Dear Mrs Conrad, I am pleased to confirm:

(a)   Your / personal credit arrangement of £2000. The present rate / of interest is 18½% per / annum, which constitutes an effective annual rate of 19. / 7%, and a monthly rate of 1 / ½%. A fee of £5 will / be charged in any quarter that the service is used. /

(b)   The possibility of a personal loan of up to / £5000 subject to the completion of the appropriate / documentation, in accordance with Consumer Credit Act requirements. Please check / before making any commitments.

If, at any time, you wish / to discuss any aspects of your banking requirements, please do / not hesitate to contact me. Yours sincerely *(127 words)*